SCHOLASTIC

Let's Find Out

My REBUS Reader

I0890050

I See a Frog!

by Joan Michael

SCHOLASTIC INC.
New York Toronto London Auckland Sydney New Delhi Hong Kong

I see a **green**  .

frog

False Tomato Frog

I see a red  .

frog

I see a yellow  .

e Poison Dart Frog

I see a **blue**  .

frog

I see an orange  .

frog

I see a black and white  .

frog

Common Frogs

I see  frogs ! Hop, hop, hop!